Usborne

Dragons
Magic Painting Book

Illustrated by
Camilla Garofano

Designed by Brenda Cole

To stop water from seeping through to the next page, unfold the flap at the back of the book and place it under the page you're about to work on.

Dip the brush into water, then brush it across the black patterns within each shape to see the paint magically appear.